THE OFFICIAL
ROTHERHAM UNITED
QUIZ BOOK

THE OFFICIAL ROTHERHAM UNITED QUIZ BOOK

Compiled by Chris Cowlin
Kevin Snelgrove and Peter Miles

Foreword by Paul Hurst

APEX PUBLISHING LTD

Hardback first published in 2009 by
Apex Publishing Ltd
PO Box 7086, Clacton on Sea, Essex, CO15 5WN, England
www.apexpublishing.co.uk

British Library Cataloguing-in-Publication Data
A catalogue record for this book
is available from the British Library

ISBN HARDBACK: 1-906358-40-0   978-1-906358-40-2

Typeset in 10.5pt Chianti Bdlt Win95BT

Cover Design: Siobhan Smith

Printed in Great Britain by the
MPG Books Group, Bodmin and King's Lynn

Author's Note:
Please can you contact me: **ChrisCowlin@btconnect.com** if you find any
mistakes/errors in this book as I would like to put them right on any
future reprints of this book. I would also like to hear from Rotherham
fans who have enjoyed the test! For more information on me and my
books please look at: **www.ChrisCowlin.com**

This book is an official product of Rotherham United Football Club

We would like to dedicate this book to:

All the players and staff who have worked for the club during their history.

FOREWORD

I feel both honoured and privileged to have been asked to write the foreword for this official Rotherham United quiz book which, I am sure, will give you many hours of enjoyment.

My relationship with the club started when I was 11 years old, training in the gym at Millmoor with dreams of becoming a professional footballer. Eight years later I signed my first professional contract, but I could not have imagined that I would go on to become the club's all time record appearance maker.

The reception I received on the day I broke the record will stay with me for the rest of my life and made it an extremely special occasion. The record will take some beating because of how football is today and I hope to hold it for quite a few years as it is an achievement I am extremely proud of.

The club have provided me with many more special memories including winning at Wembley, playing in the Championship and granting me a testimonial which I will be forever grateful.

Both on and off the pitch I have made some very good friends and met some wonderful people. My affection with the club has grown stronger and stronger over the years and it will always have a special place in my heart.

This book is a must for all Millers followers, young and old, and will test even the most diehard fans. Whether travelling to an away game or spending a night at home with friends or family, it will provide you with hours of fun. I am certain some of the Mf ... questions will leave you scratching your head but most of all they will have you recalling some great times while following Rotherham United.

All it remains for me to say is a big thank you to all the fans that have supported me in my career, keep up your loyal support of the club and happy reading.

Up The Millers!

Paul Hurst

INTRODUCTION

I would first of all like to thank Paul Hurst for writing the foreword to this book. I am very grateful for his help on this project.

I would also like to thank all the people who have provided a comment and/or review on this book (these can be found at the back of the book).

I would also like to thank Mark Hitchens at Rotherham United Football Club for his help during the books compilation. A special mention of thanks must go to Les Payne at The Star and Green 'Un, Sheffield, for checking our questions.

I hope you enjoy this book. Hopefully it should bring back some wonderful memories!

It was great working with Kevin Snelgrove and Peter Miles again, between us I hope we have given you a selection of easy, medium and hard questions.

In closing, I would like to thank all my friends and family for encouraging me to complete this book.

Chris Cowlin

Best wishes
Chris Cowlin

www.apexpublishing.co.uk

HISTORY OF THE CLUB

1. In what year were Rotherham United founded?

2. Which two clubs amalgamated to form Rotherham United?

3. What is Rotherham United's nickname?

4. Where did Rotherham United play their home games up until May 2008?

5. Who was Rotherham United's first ever manager, in charge from 1925 to 1929?

6. In 1955 Rotherham finished third on goal difference in League Division 2, denying them promotion to the top flight, but which two teams gained promotion?

7. Rotherham won the Division 3 title in 1981, but which local rivals were runners-up?

8. In 1889 Rotherham signed the first black professional footballer. What was his name?

9. On 16 January 2002 in the FA Cup 3rd round Rotherham took £106,182 in gate receipts for a match against which team?

10. At the start of the 2008/09 League 2 season how many points were deducted from Rotherham United?

WHO AM I?

11. *I was born in 1951, started as an apprentice, and later kept goal for Preston and Wigan.*

12. *My middle name is St Lloyd and I was a St Kitts international.*

13. *I was born in Clydebank and also kept goal for Sheffield United, Blackpool and West Ham.*

14. *I was born in Brighton, played from 1980-82 and also served at Brighton, Millwall and Wolves.*

15. *I have one Welsh cap, I finished my playing career at Millmoor and I also managed the club.*

16. *I am a former Liverpool trainee, I joined Rotherham from Bolton in 1994, and later I played for Mansfield and Exeter City.*

17. *I was born in Rotherham and scored 80 League goals in 321 games for the club before joining Hull City.*

18. *I was born in Hitchin and played for Kidderminster, Southend, Rushden and Chester before joining The Millers in 2008.*

19. *I joined Rotherham in 1984, having played for Barnsley, Sheffield Wednesday and Southampton, and left Millmoor in 1986 for York.*

20. *I joined The Millers from Denaby United and left for Nottingham Forest, where I scored 123 times in 182 games.*

CLUB RECORDS

21. Rotherham United's record attendance of 25,170 was in a Division 2 match on 13 December 1952 against which Yorkshire team?

22. In a Division 3 North match on 25 August 1928 Rotherham were beaten 11-1 by which team?

23. Who made 459 League appearances for Rotherham from 1946 to 1962?

24. Who scored five goals for Rotherham in the FA Cup 1st round on 25 November 1950 against Darlington?

25. On 26 May 1947 in Division 3 North Rotherham recorded their record League victory against Oldham Athletic. What was the score?

26. How many League goals did Rotherham score in Division 3 North in season 1946/47 –94, 104 or 114?

27. Who scored 130 League goals for Rotherham from 1946 to 1956?

28. How many games did Rotherham win in February 1982 – 5, 7 or 9?

29. In 1991 Rotherham were the first team to win a penalty shootout in the FA Cup, against which opponents?

30. In 1961 Rotherham were the first team to score in the final against Aston Villa in which competition?

THE LEAGUE CUP

31.   Who were Rotherham's first opponents in this
        competition?

32.   Who scored the club's first goal in this competition?

33.   Who put Rotherham out of the Milk Cup in the 3rd
        round in November 1982?

34.   The Millers drew 4-4 with which team in the 1st round
        of the Littlewoods Cup in 1987?

35.   The Millers lost 7-2 on aggregate in the League Cup
        1st round in season 1975/76 to which club?

36.   Which side took The Millers to penalties in a 1st round
        replay in 1977/78?

37.   Who scored a League Cup hat-trick in a 1978 tie
        against Hartlepool?

38.   What round did Rotherham reach in 1983/44 before
        losing 4-2 at home to Walsall?

39.   Against which side did Rotherham come back from a
        1-4 1st leg deficit in 1995?

40.   Who put The Millers out of the Carling Cup in the 2nd
        round in 2006/07?

CLUB HONOURS

Match up the honour with the year it was achieved by Rotherham United

41.	League Cup runners-up	1989
42.	Auto Windscreens Shield winners	1951
43.	Division 3 champions	1992
44.	Division 3 North champions	2000
45.	Division 2 runners-up	1961
46.	Division 3 runners-up	1948
47.	Division 4 champions	1968
48.	Division 3 North runners-up	2001
49.	Division 4 runners-up	1981
50.	Reached the FA Cup 5th round	1996

PAUL WARNE

51. In what position did Paul play for Rotherham?

52. In what year did Paul join Rotherham from Wigan Athletic?

53. How many League goals did Paul score in his Rotherham career – 26, 27 or 28?

54. Which Rotherham manager signed Paul for the club?

55. Against which team did Paul score the only goal, and also his last goal for the club, in a 1-0 home League win during March 2005?

56. In which year was Paul born in Norwich – 1971, 1972 or 1973?

57. True or false: Paul scored a brace on his Rotherham League debut?

58. Following on from the previous question, against which club did Paul play on his Rotherham debut in a 3-1 home win?

59. How many League goals did Paul score during 1999/2000, his first season at the club?

60. Which club did Paul join in 2005 when he left Rotherham?

WHERE DID THEY GO? – 1

*Match up the player with the club he joined
on leaving Rotherham United*

61.	Les Bradd	**Cardiff City**
62.	Ronnie Moore	**Nottingham Forest**
63.	Clive Mendonca	**Chesterfield**
64.	Neil Warnock	**Exeter City**
65.	Alan Crawford	**Notts County**
66.	Deon Burton	**Charlton Athletic**
67.	Alan Lee	**Sheffield United**
68.	Bob Delgado	**Sheffield Wednesday**
69.	Ronnie Burke	**Hartlepool United**
70.	Wally Ardron	**Chester City**

2008/2009

71.   Who managed Rotherham during this season?

72.   From which club did Rotherham sign Richard Barker, initially on loan and then permanently in January 2009?

73.   Which team did Rotherham beat 1-0 on the opening day of the League season, during August 2008?

74.   Following on from the previous question, which forward scored the only goal in the game on his debut?

75.   True or false: Rotherham were unbeaten in the League during their four matches in August 2008?

76.   Which Rotherham player wore the no. 14 shirt during this season?

77.   Which two 'Jamie's' scored for Rotherham in a 2-0 home win against Gillingham during February 2009?

78.   What was the score when Rotherham played Grimsby Town at home in the League during October 2008?

79.   Which Irish midfielder scored Rotherham's only goal in a 1-0 away win against Lincoln City during February 2009?

80.   Which goalkeeper signed for Hull City when he left Rotherham in August 2008?

MANAGERS – 1

*Match up the manager with the period he was
in charge at Rotherham United*

81.	Danny Bergara	*1979-81*
82.	Billy Heald	*1958-62*
83.	Ronnie Moore	*1983-85*
84.	Alan Knill	*1973-79*
85.	Ian Porterfield	*1925-29*
86.	Reg Freeman	*1996-97*
87.	Tom Johnston	*1934-52*
88.	Jimmy McAnearney	*2005-07*
89.	George Kerr	*1997-2005*
90.	Jimmy McGuigan	*1968-73*

2007/2008

91. With which team did Rotherham share a 0-0 draw on the opening day of the League season?

92. Who was the Rotherham manager this season?

93. Which goalkeeper played in all 46 League matches for Rotherham this season?

94. True or false: Rotherham were unbeaten in their five matches in December 2007?

95. Name the two players that scored for The Millers in the 2-1 home win against Chesterfield during March 2008.

96. Who was Rotherham's highest League scorer with 11 goals this season?

97. In which position in the League did Rotherham finish – 7th, 8th or 9th?

98. Which Rotherham player scored a brace in a 3-0 home League win on New Year's Day 2008?

99. Which team did Rotherham beat 1-0 at home on the last day of the League season?

100. Following on from the previous question, which forward scored the only goal in the game?

NATIONALITIES – 1

Match up the player with his nationality

101.	Shaun Goater	Welsh
102.	Toumani Diagouraga	Irish
103.	Adem Poric	German
104.	Jim Dobbin	French
105.	Eugen Bopp	St Lucian
106.	Bobby Mimms	Australian
107.	Bob Delgado	Bermudian
108.	Earl Jean	Welsh
109.	Ray Mielczarek	Scottish
110.	Jim McDonagh	English

LEAGUE GOALS

Match up the player with his Millers' League goal tally

111.	Wally Ardron	64 goals
112.	Jack Grainger	56 goals
113.	Alan Kirkman	98 goals
114.	Ronnie Burke	45 goals
115.	Trevor Phillips	70 goals
116.	Alan Crawford	112 goals
117.	Albert Bennett	123 goals
118.	Shaun Goater	80 goals
119.	Ian Wilson	49 goals
120.	Jack Shaw	58 goals

WHERE DID THEY COME FROM? – 1

Match up the player with the club from which he joined Rotherham United

121.	Scott Minto	**Walsall**
122.	Shaun Goater	**Watford**
123.	Mark Burchill	**Arsenal**
124.	Leo Fortune-West	**Manchester United**
125.	Andy Todd	**Wigan Athletic**
126.	Paolo Vernazza	**Brentford**
127.	Paul Warne	**Wolverhampton Wanderers**
128.	Mark Robins	**West Ham United**
129.	Paul Blades	**Dunfermline Athletic**
130.	Jim Furnell	**Accrington Stanley**

LEGENDS

Rearrange the letters to reveal the name of a club legend

131.   RYERG EFSROT

132.   NHOJ KRENBIC

133.   YOR TARMBEL

134.   EVDA SAWNOT

135.   MYMJI DURD

136.   LANA EEL

137.   KRAM NIBSOR

138.   UNASH ROTAGE

139.   YONT ORNEWT

140.   AKCJ WASH

LEAGUE POSITIONS - 1

*Match up the season/points with Rotherham's
League finishing position*

141.	2000/01, 91 points	23rd
142.	1951/52, 42 points	16th
143.	1965/66, 46 points	20th
144.	1982/83, 45 points	2nd
145.	1993/94, 58 points	8th
146.	1996/97, 35 points	9th
147.	1954/55, 54 points	14th
148.	1962/63, 40 points	15th
149.	1995/96, 56 points	7th
150.	1959/60, 47 points	3rd

ATTENDANCES

151. How many people watched the League Cup final 1st leg against Aston Villa in 1961 - 11,097, 12,226 or 12,933?

152. How many people watched the League Cup final 2nd leg against Aston Villa in 1961 - 31,201, 33,719 or 35,492?

153. Which FA Cup opponents attracted a 50,040 gate in January 1951?

154. At which ground were Rotherham playing in September 1951 when 54,846 turned up?

155. How many people watched the 2002 Worthington Cup tie at Wimbledon – 664, 1,064 or 1,664?

156. True or false: Millmoor's last five-figure gate was 11,455 against Nottingham Forest in 2003?

157. A 2003/04 League match against which team attracted a gate of 34,483?

158. What crowd witnessed the Carling Cup tie against Arsenal in 2003 - 27,451, 28,022 or 28,549?

159. In the 2004/05 Championship season, an away game against which side got the biggest gate of 30,900?

160. Which Rotherham match attracted the only five-figure crowd of the 2007/08 season?

LEAGUE POSITIONS - 2

*Match up the season/points with Rotherham's
League finishing position*

161.	1968/69, 45 points	5th
162.	1985/86, 57 points	2nd
163.	1990/91, 42 points	18th
164.	1999/2000, 84 points	8th
165.	1976/77, 59 points	11th
166.	1972/73, 41 points	23rd
167.	1998/99, 73 points	1st
168.	1970/71, 50 points	14th
169.	1980/81, 61 points	21st
170.	1983/84, 54 points	4th

2006/2007

171. How many League wins did The Millers achieve this season – 13, 15 or 17?

172. Which team were beaten 5-1 at Millmoor in October 2006?

173. Which side did Rotherham beat in the opening round of the Carling Cup?

174. Which match attracted a crowd of 27,875?

175. Who was Rotherham's top goalscorer with 15 League goals?

176. How many points were the club docked for entering a Company Voluntary Arrangement?

177. Who were the club's shirt sponsors this season?

178. Which side put The Millers out of the FA Cup in the 1st round?

179. Which club signed Lee Williamson and Will Hoskins?

180. How many of Rotherham's 64 League and Cup goals were penalties - 5, 6 or 7?

SQUAD NUMBERS 2008/2009 – 1

Match up the player with his squad number

181.	Ryan Taylor	3
182.	Ian Sharps	16
183.	Andy Todd	21
184.	Andy Warrington	5
185.	Jamie Yates	8
186.	Pablo Mills	14
187.	Peter Holmes	20
188.	Mark Lynch	7
189.	Michael Cummins	25
190.	Tom Cahill	1

GOALKEEPERS

191. Who kept goal in the two legs of the 1961 League Cup final?

192. Which keeper played 248 League games between 1985 and 1990?

193. From which club did Bobby Mimms sign?

194. Which Manchester United keeper played on loan at Millmoor in 1996/97?

195. Which keeper played 45 of the 46 League games in season 1978/79?

196. Who kept goal in the 1996 Auto Windscreens Shield final?

197. Which keeper played 96 League and Cup matches between August 2001 and April 2003?

198. From which club did Carl Muggleton arrive on loan in 1995?

199. In what country was Roy Tunks born?

200. Which keeper made 104 League appearances between 1989 and 1994?

WHERE DID THEY GO? – 2

*Match up the player with the club he joined on
leaving Rotherham United*

201.	Will Hoskins	York City
202.	Bobby Ham	Plymouth Argyle
203.	Robbie Stockdale	Doncaster Rovers
204.	David Artell	Hull City
205.	Tommy Tynan	Watford
206.	Jackie Bestall	Sunderland
207.	Don Weston	Mansfield Town
208.	Terry Farmer	Grimsby Town
209.	Darren Byfield	Bradford City
210.	Jim Dobbin	Leeds United

TONY TOWNER

211. In what position did Tony play during his career?

212. At which club did Tony start his professional football career in 1976?

213. In what year did Tony join Rotherham United from Millwall?

214. Following on from the previous question, which other Millwall player joined Rotherham in a joint deal with Tony?

215. Which Rotherham manager brought Tony to the club and gave him his debut?

216. How many League goals did Tony score during his Rotherham career – 1, 6 or 11?

217. In which year was Tony born – 1953, 1954 or 1955?

218. For which club did Tony play between 1984 and 1986?

219. Which team did Tony join when he left Rotherham United?

220. What was Tony's nickname at Rotherham?

MANAGERS – 2

Match up the manager with the period he was in charge at Rotherham United

221.	Billy McEwan	1930-33
222.	Mick Harford	1965-67
223.	Stan Davies	1981-83
224.	Tommy Docherty	2005
225.	Emlyn Hughes	1929-30
226.	Andy Smailes	1962-65
227.	Billy Heald	1988-91
228.	Norman Hunter	1952-58
229.	Jack Mansell	1967-68
230.	Danny Williams	1985-87

UNUSUAL SOURCES

*Match up the player with the club from which
he joined Rotherham United*

231.	Carl Airey	Manvers Main Colliery
232.	José Miranda	Charleroi
233.	John Hunter	Dunscroft
234.	Jack Edwards	Parkgate Welfare
235.	Barry Burns	Felgueiras
236.	Dennis Churms	Owen and Dyson
237.	James Marsden	Coltness United
238.	Jock Quairney	Atlas and Norfolk
239.	Danny Bolton	Girvan Juniors
240.	Roy Ironside	Spurley Hey

WHERE DID THEY COME FROM? – 2

Match up the player with the club from which he joined Rotherham United

241. Derek Holmes   **Lincoln City**

242. Neil Cutler   **Port Vale**

243. Jimmy Rudd   **Stockport County**

244. Michael Jeffrey   **Tranmere Rovers**

245. Ian Sharps   **Scunthorpe United**

246. Richie Barker   **Carlisle United**

247. Michael Proctor   **Newcastle United**

248. Tommy Spencer   **Leeds United**

249. Alan Knill   **Sunderland**

250. Lee Glover   **Macclesfield Town**

1990s

251. The Millers went out to which side in the FA Cup 4th round in 1990/91?

252. Who was the top goalscorer in the 1993/94 season with 19 League goals?

253. In what position did The Millers finish in the 1992/93 season - 8th, 11th or 13th?

254. What was the crowd for the 1996 Auto Windscreens Shield final – 25,523, 30,325 or 35,235?

255. Following on from the previous question, who scored Rotherham's goals in the 2-1 win against Shrewsbury Town?

256. Following on again, in the run to the final Rotherham beat Wigan 4-1 on penalties, but who was The Millers' keeper that night?

257. As holders of the Shield, The Millers were knocked out of the 1996/97 competition in the 1st round by which team?

258. Which non-League side were beaten by Rotherham 6-0 in the FA Cup 2nd round in 1997/98?

259. Which player played in all 92 League games of the 1998/99 and 1999/2000 seasons?

260. Which two players scored double-figure League goals in the 1999/2000 campaign?

SQUAD NUMBERS 2008/2009 – 2

Match up the player with his squad number

261.	Dale Tonge	19
262.	Mark Hudson	6
263.	Steven Cann	15
264.	Mark Burchill	2
265.	Nick Fenton	11
266.	Marc Joseph	30
267.	Jamie Green	4
268.	Danny Harrison	9
269.	Stephen Brogan	10
270.	Alex Rhodes	12

2005/2006

271.   Who started this season as The Millers' boss?

272.   Which club did Rotherham defeat in the League on their own ground for the first time in 33 years during August?

273.   Which side did The Millers beat 3-2 on penalties in the 1st round of the LDV Trophy?

274.   Who put Rotherham out of the Carling Cup?

275.   Who was the top League goalscorer with 12 goals despite leaving the club in December?

276.   Which away game attracted a gate of 20,123?

277.   Which player started the most League games with 42?

278.   By what scoreline did The Millers lose to Mansfield in the FA Cup 1st round?

279.   Following on from the previous question, which former Miller scored a last-minute winner for The Stags?

280.   Rotherham used which two goalkeepers during this campaign?

FA CUP WINS

Match up the season/round with the result

281.	2000/01, round 2	Grantham 1-4 Rotherham United
282.	1992/93, round 2	Aston Villa 0-1 Rotherham United
283.	1978/79, round 1	Rotherham United 2-0 Arsenal
284.	1967/68, round 4	Rotherham United 2-1 Coventry City
285.	1985/86, round 2	Rotherham United 1-0 Northampton Town
286.	1950/51, round 3	Rotherham United 4-1 Burnley
287.	1959/60, round 3 2nd replay	Rotherham United 3-0 Workington
288.	1970/71, round 2	Rotherham United 2-1 Southampton
289.	2001/02, round 3	Rotherham United 1-0 Hull City
290.	1933/34, round 2	Rotherham United 2-1 Doncaster Rovers

TOMMY DOCHERTY

291. In which year was Tommy born – 1928, 1930 or 1932?

292. Where was Tommy born - ?

293. What was Tommy's first club as a player?

294. Which club did Tommy join for £28,000 in August 1958?

295. Who did Tommy replace as Rotherham manager?

296. Tommy joined which club as manager after his short stint in charge at Rotherham?

297. Which European club did Tommy manage in 1970/71?

298. How many full caps did Tommy gain for Scotland?

299. Which two Australian clubs did Tommy manage?

300. Which club did Tommy manage between October 1987 and February 1988?

PLAYING YEARS AT THE CLUB – 1

Match up the player with the period he spent at Rotherham United

301.	Paul Hurst	1964-68
302.	Jim McDonagh	2000-03
303.	Tony Towner	1968-79
304.	Jack Shaw	1980-83
305.	Trevor Phillips	1954-65
306.	Johnny Quinn	1946-53
307.	Peter Madden	1970-76
308.	Roy Lambert	1967-72
309.	John Galley	1993-2008
310.	Alan Lee	1955-66

MILLMOOR

311. In what year was the stadium opened?

312. Two stands were moved to Millmoor from which previous Rotherham County ground?

313. What other sport took place at Millmoor in the early 1930s?

314. Why was the Tivoli End so called?

315. True or false: at 115 x 75 yards, Millmoor had the smallest Football League pitch?

316. Which end had scrapyard cranes peering over the roof?

317. How many years did Rotherham play their home games at Millmoor before they moved to the Don Valley Stadium?

318. In what year were floodlights first used, in a match against Bristol Rovers?

319. Who owned the ground when the club were forced to relocate to Don Valley?

320. Which unusual plant was discovered growing in the area of the new stand in 2006?

TOP GOALSCORERS

Match up the player with the number of goals he scored for Rotherham United

321.	Gladstone Guest	46
322.	Albert Bennett	56
323.	Wally Ardron	130
324.	Jack Shaw	86
325.	Trevor Phillips	123
326.	John Galley	98
327.	Jack Grainger	52
328.	Shaun Goater	64
329.	Ronnie Moore	112
330.	Ronnie Burke	82

JOHN BRECKIN

331.   Where in Yorkshire was John born – Sheffield,
       Rotherham or Doncaster?

332.   In which year was John born - 1951, 1952 or 1953?

333.   Against which club did John make his League debut for
       Rotherham in January 1972?

334.   John scored his first goal for The Millers in June 1973
       against which team?

335.   John was loaned out to which club in 1972/73?

336.   Which club did John join in February 1983?

337.   How many League appearances did John make for
       Rotherham - 391, 409 or 426?

338.   With which club did John finish his League career?

339.   What was my first 'ever-present' season for
       Rotherham, when I played all 50 matches?

340.   Who brought me back to Millmoor as coach in
       2003/04?

POSITIONS THEY PLAYED – 1

Match up the player with the position in which he played for Rotherham United

341.	Jack Selkirk	Striker
342.	Jock Quairney	Centre forward
343.	Norman Noble	Goalkeeper
344.	Shaun Goater	Winger
345.	Jim McDonagh	Right back
346.	Dave Watson	Left back
347.	Jack Grainger	Goalkeeper
348.	Trevor Phillips	Defender
349.	Jim Breckin	Striker
350.	John Galley	Central defender

2008/2009

351. Who scored the first competitive goal for The Millers at Don Valley in the 1-0 win against Lincoln City?

352. Which side did Rotherham defeat on penalties in the 2nd round of the Carling Cup?

353. Which team did United defeat in their opening Johnstone's Paint Trophy match?

354. Which side eventually put The Millers out of the Carling Cup?

355. Which much-travelled striker joined the club from Wrexham during the summer?

356. Tom Cahill was loaned out to which non-League club?

357. From which club was Jason Taylor signed in January 2009?

358. Omar Garcia joined the club in September 2008, but for which two Spanish clubs has he played?

359. Which team put The Millers out of the FA Cup?

360. Which side were beaten by Rotherham 5-1 away during March 2009?

PLAYING YEARS AT THE CLUB – 2

*Match up the player with the period he
spent at Rotherham United*

361.	Jack Grainger	1998-2005
362.	Bobby Williamson	1961-65
363.	Shaun Goater	1971-83
364.	Gerry Forrest (1st spell)	1988-90
365.	Lol Morgan	1980-83
366.	Mike Pollitt	1968-70
367.	Ronnie Moore	1954-64
368.	John Breckin	1945-57
369.	Dave Watson	1989-96
370.	Albert Bennett	1977-85

WHO WERE WE PLAYING?

You are given a ground and a year, but which team were The Millers playing?

371.   Brewery Field in 1977

372.   Manor Park in 1966

373.   Tower Athletic Ground in 1946

374.   Seedhill in 1928

375.   Borough Park in 1969

376.   Redheugh Park in 1931

377.   Westfield Lane in 1985

378.   Portland Park in 1928

379.   Marston Road in 1975

380.   York Street in 1980

TOP LEAGUE APPEARANCES

*Match up the player with the number of appearances
he made for Rotherham United*

381.	Jack Selkirk	292
382.	Danny Williams	352
383.	Paul Hurst	427
384.	Gerry Forrest	301
385.	John Breckin	494
386.	Jack Grainger	492
387.	Norman Noble	308
388.	Mike Pollitt	467
389.	Peter Madden	311
390.	Darren Garner	394

LEAGUE DEBUTS

Match up the player with the year he made his debut for Rotherham United

391.	John Edwards	1955
392.	Des Hazel	1993
393.	Paul Hurst	1977
394.	Jack Grainger	1946
395.	Roy Lambert	1956
396.	Gerry Forrest	1957
397.	Lol Morgan	1979
398.	Peter Madden	1971
399.	Ray Mountford	1988
400.	John Breckin	1947

POSITIONS THEY PLAYED – 2

Match up the player with the position in which he played

401.	Jack Edwards	Striker
402.	Paul Stancliffe	Left back
403.	Gerry Forrest	Wing half
404.	Wally Ardron	Goalkeeper
405.	Paul Hurst	Striker
406.	Peter Madden	Centre forward
407.	Mike Pollitt	Defender
408.	Mark Robins	Right back
409.	Jack Shaw	Centre half
410.	Lol Morgan	Central defender

1980s

411. Who was the Rotherham manager at the turn of the decade?

412. Who were Rotherham's first opponents of the 1980s - Colchester, Chesterfield or Southend?

413. Who was The Millers' leading League goalscorer in season 1982/83?

414. How many goals did Ronnie Moore score in 1981/82 – 20, 22 or 24?

415. Which future League club did Rotherham beat in the FA Cup in November 1980?

416. Who managed Rotherham between 1983 and 1985?

417. Which signing from Grimsby scored in his first three League games for The Millers in 1983/84?

418. Rotherham lost 7-0 to which side in February 1985?

419. Who scored a hat-trick for Rotherham in a 4-1 defeat of Swindon in February 1986?

420. Who scored a hat-trick for Rotherham in a 5-3 win at Carlisle in December 1986?

MATCH THE YEAR – 1

Match up the event with the year it took place

421. Rotherham began playing their
      home games at Sheffield's
      Don Valley Stadium   1949

422. Lee Glover signs for Rotherham United   1999

423. T-Mobile became Rotherham's sponsors
      for the first time   2008

424. Shaun Goater joined Rotherham United   1997

425. Clive Mendonca was born   2002

426. Rotherham ended the season with
      91 points in Division 2   1971

427. Ronnie Moore became manager
      of The Millers   1968

428. The Millers were the runners-up in
      Division 3 North   2001

429. Rotherham escaped relegation on
      goal difference   1996

430. Scott Minto was born   1989

SIGNED FROM WHERE?

Match up the player up with the club from which
he signed for Rotherham United

431.	Mick Pickering	Sunderland
432.	Earl Jean	Sheffield United
433.	Jimmy Mullen	Aston Villa
434.	Andy Roscoe	Watford
435.	Clive Mendonca	Ipswich Town
436.	Michael Proctor	Sheffield Wednesday
437.	Toumani Diagouraga	Accrington Stanley
438.	Julian Baudet	Bolton Wanderers
439.	Trevor Berry	Charlton Athletic
440.	Andy Todd	Oldham Athletic

MATCH THE YEAR – 2

Match up the event with the year it took place

441.	Reuben Reid joined The Millers	*1996*
442.	Rotherham reached the FA Cup 5th round	*1981*
443.	Danny Williams left Rotherham United	*2004*
444.	Tony Towner was born	*1970*
445.	Emlyn Hughes joined Rotherham from Wolverhampton Wanderers	*1966*
446.	Jim Furnell left The Millers to join Plymouth Argyle	*2008*
447.	Neil Warnock joined Rotherham from Chesterfield	*1955*
448.	Chris Sedgwick made his 244th League appearance for the club	*1976*
449.	Andy Warrington was born	*1953*
450.	Nigel Jemson came to Rotherham on loan and made 16 League appearances, scoring 5 goals	*1969*

1970s

451. Which Millmoor youngster played for England Youth in 1970?

452. Who was sold to Sheffield Wednesday for £40,000 in December 1970?

453. Which team did The Millers beat 6-2 in the opening round of the FA Cup in 1970/71?

454. Which Welsh defender joined Rotherham from Huddersfield for £25,000 in January 1971?

455. Which three clubs did Rotherham play in the 1972 European tour?

456. Who scored two goals and conceded three in a 7-2 defeat at home to Bournemouth in 1972?

457. Against which team did Rotherham record an 8-1 victory away in September 1973?

458. Who scored 31 League and Cup goals in 1976/77?

459. Which two non-League sides did The Millers defeat in the FA Cup in the 1977/78 campaign?

460. Who did Ian Porterfield succeed as manager of Rotherham?

CAPS FOR MY COUNTRY

Match up the player with the number of international caps he won

461. Shaun Goater   1 cap for England

462. Dave Watson   6 caps for Scotland

463. Alan Knill   36 caps for Bermuda

464. Bruce Dyer   10 caps for Republic of
                                 Ireland

465. Alan Lee   65 caps for England

466. Emlyn Hughes   1 cap for Wales

467. Mark Burchill   34 caps for Northern
                                 Ireland

468. Jackie Bestall   1 cap for Montserrat

469. Colin Murdock   24 caps for Republic of
                                 Ireland

470. Jim McDonagh   62 caps for England

YEAR OF BIRTH

Match up the player with his year of birth

471. Jack Grainger   1958

472. Graham Coughlan   1979

473. Gerry Gow   1957

474. Roy Ironside   1974

475. Barry Cowdrill   1967

476. Dave Gwyther   1971

477. Phil Gridelet   1952

478. Scott Minto   1924

479. Paul Stancliffe   1948

480. Guy Branston   1935

NATIONALITIES – 2

Match up the player with his nationality

481.	Omar Garcia	Welsh
482.	Steven Cann	French
483.	Mark Burchill	Montserratian
484.	Michael Cummins	Jamaican
485.	Lee Williamson	Scottish
486.	Bruce Dyer	Northern Irish
487.	Alan Knill	Spanish
488.	Colin Murdock	English
489.	Dick Habbin	Welsh
490.	Leandre Griffit	Irish

PHIL HENSON

491. With which club did Phil turn professional?

492. Which club did Phil join for £50,000 in February 1975?

493. For which Dutch club did Phil briefly play?

494. In which year was Phil born – 1951, 1952 or 1953?

495. From which club did Phil join Rotherham?

496. Phil helped The Millers to win which League Championship in 1980/81?

497. Who signed Phil for Rotherham?

498. Phil was assistant manager to whom at Millmoor?

499. To what position in Division 4 did Phil guide The Millers in 1991/92?

500. Who took charge of Rotherham after Phil left?

TRANSFERS

Match up the player with his transfer fee

501.	Mike Pollitt to Rotherham United 2001	£150,000
502.	Albert Bennett to Newcastle United 1965	£175,000
503.	Deon Burton to Rotherham United 2005	£75,000
504.	Clive Mendonca to Rotherham United 1988	£150,000
505.	Alan Lee to Rotherham United 2000	Free
506.	Dave Watson to Sunderland 1970	£30,000
507.	Leo Fortune-West to Rotherham United 1999	£100,000
508.	Jim McDonagh to Bolton Wanderers 1976	£35,000
509.	Shaun Goater to Bristol City 1996	£27,000
510.	Darren Garner to Rotherham United 1995	£35,000

HAT-TRICKS

511.   Which player scored four goals against Millwall in August 2002?

512.   Who scored Rotherham's first League hat-trick in January 1926?

513.   How many times did Wally Ardron score four goals in a Millers' League match?

514.   Who scored successive League hat-tricks in 1989/90?

515.   Who scored four goals in a game against Chester in August 1987?

516.   Which two players scored League hat-tricks in 1998/99?

517.   Who scored all three Rotherham goals at Burnley in a 3-3 draw in April 1997?

518.   How many hat-tricks did Shaun Goater score for The Millers?

519.   How many hat-tricks did Wally Ardron bag for Rotherham?

520.   Who scored three goals against Lincoln in January 2008?

SHAUN GOATER

521. Shaun was born in Hamilton, Bermuda, on 25 February in which year – 1968, 1970 or 1972?

522. From which club did Shaun join Rotherham United in 1989?

523. What honour was Shaun awarded in 2003 for his services to sports?

524. How many appearances did Shaun make for Rotherham in all competitions – 262, 282 or 302?

525. At which English club did Shaun finish his professional career in 2006 before moving back to Bermuda to play for Bermuda Hogges?

526. How many League goals did Shaun score for The Millers – 50, 60 or 70?

527. Which team did Shaun join for £500,000 in August 2003?

528. In the close season of 1996 which Spanish club put an offer in for Shaun?

529. Which club did Shaun only make one League appearance for on loan in 1993?

530. True or false: Shaun was awarded the freedom of Bermuda in June 2000 and this was marked by a national Shaun Goater day?

DON VALLEY

531. In what year were the World Student Games held at Don Valley?

532. When was the stadium opened?

533. Which firm built the stadium?

534. What Channel 4 reality TV programme was held at Don Valley?

535. What was the cost of constructing the stadium - £29 million, £33 million or £40 million?

536. Other than Rotherham, what three other sports teams used the stadium in 2008/09?

537. How tall is each floodlight pylon - 29 metres, 36 metres or 45 metres?

538. Who made a new world record javelin throw at Don Valley in August 1993?

539. Who were The Millers' first opponents at the ground on 19 July 2008?

540. Who were the first League visitors to Don Valley?

DARREN GARNER

541. Darren was born on 10 December 1971 in which West Country city?

542. At which club did Darren start his professional career in 1989?

543. In what position does Darren play?

544. Darren transferred to The Millers in June 1995 from which non-League club?

545. How many League appearances did Darren make for The Millers – 239 (16), 249 (16) or 259 (16)?

546. After ten years with Rotherham Darren moved on a free transfer to which club in 2005?

547. How many League goals did Darren score for The Millers – 23, 33 or 43?

548. Why did Darren never play a game for Rotherham in season 2001/02?

549. Which three non-League clubs from Cornwall did Darren join in 2007?

550. Which post did Darren take up for the first time on 14 February 2009

BIG WINS

551.   In 1977 Rotherham beat which non-League club 6-0 in the FA Cup?

552.   In 1985 who were also beaten 6-0 in the FA Cup by The Millers?

553.   Who were beaten 6-0 on their own ground in the opening match of the 2002/03 season?

554.   In which year did Rotherham beat Oldham 8-0 in a Division 3 North encounter?

555.   At which club did The Millers record a 5-0 Boxing Day win in 1999?

556.   Which club did Rotherham defeat 5-1 in September 1990?

557.   Which club were beaten by The Millers 7-0 in January 1930?

558.   Which side did The Millers beat 5-0 in a League Cup 1st round 2nd leg tie in 1995?

559.   Which team were beaten 7-2 at Millmoor in September 1947?

560.   True or false, The Millers scored six goals in three successive home League matches in season 1946/47?

MARK ROBINS

561. Mark was born in Ashton-under-Lyne on 22 December in which year – 1965, 1967 or 1969?

562. At which club did Mark start his career as a trainee in December 1986?

563. In August 1992 Mark was transferred to Norwich City, for what fee?

564. Which club did Norwich City beat 4-2 on the opening day of the very first Premier League season, with Mark scoring two goals for the Canaries?

565. Which manager did Mark replace at Rotherham?

566. In his three years at the club how many League appearances did Mark make for The Millers – 64 (23), 84 (23) or 104 (23)?

567. Which honour did Mark win with Manchester United in 1990?

568. How many appearances did Mark make for England at Under 21 level, scoring seven goals?

569. How many League goals did Mark score for The Millers – 44, 54 or 64?

570. At which non-League did Mark finish his playing career in 2005?

1960s

571. Which side did Rotherham beat in the semi-final of the first League Cup competition in 1960/61?

572. Who scored seven League goals in the first four matches of season 1961/62?

573. Who scored 23 goals in 29 League matches in season 1962/63?

574. Who played all 48 League and Cup games in season 1966/67?

575. Which side were beaten 4-3 at Millmoor in the opening game of season 1969/70?

576. In what season were Rotherham relegated to Division 3?

577. Jack Mansell left Millmoor to manage which club in 1967?

578. From which club did Johnny Quinn sign for The Millers for £27,500 in November 1967?

579. For what then record fee was Ian Butler sold to Hull City in January 1965?

580. Where did the club go on tour at the end of the 1960/61 season?

RONNIE MOORE

581. Ronnie was born on 29 January 1953 in which north-west city?

582 . In 1982 Ronnie won the League Division 2 Golden Boot as top goalscorer, with how many goals?

583. At which club did Ronnie start his professional career in 1971, making 324 League appearances for them and scoring 78 goals?

584. From which club did Ronnie join Rotherham United in 1980?

585. How many League goals did Ronnie score for The Millers – 42, 52 or 62?

586. In his three seasons with Rotherham United how many League appearances did Ronnie make – 105, 115 or 125?

587. In his professional career Ronnie played in two positions, one as a striker but what was the other?

588. For which club did Ronnie play in season 1985/86, scoring 9 League goals in 43 League appearances?

589. In September 2006 Ronnie took over as manager of which club, where his son Ian is a striker?

590. Ronnie succeeded which Rotherham United manager in May 1997?

POT LUCK – 1

591. In what season did the club first compete as Rotherham United?

592. Which team provided Rotherham County's final opposition on 2 May 1925?

593. What was Rotherham County's name between 1877 and 1905?

594. Which player won 14 caps for his country while at Millmoor?

595. Who became Rotherham's youngest player when he took to the pitch against Scunthorpe in 1984?

596. What nationality was Nick Viljoen?

597. Who managed The Millers during the 1987/88 season?

598. What League did Rotherham Town win in 1891/92?

599. Which chairman/owner left Rotherham with £250,000 of debts in 1983?

600. Who transferred to Rotherham from Millwall for £150,000 in August 1980?

PAUL HURST

601. Paul was born on 25 September 1974 in which Yorkshire city?

602. What was Paul's nickname at Rotherham?

603. How many League appearances did Paul make for The Millers – 385 (51), 395 (51) or 405 (51)?

604. In 2008 Paul spent a month on loan to which Conference Premier club while he regained his fitness?

605. In what position does Paul play?

606. How many League goals did Paul score for The Millers – 3, 13 or 23?

607. Which honour did Paul win with Rotherham United in 1996?

608. How many appearances in all competitions (a Rotherham record) did Paul make – 454, 474 or 494?

609. At which club did Paul start his professional career in 1993?

610. With which club did Paul have a trial in 2008?

LEAGUE GOALSCORERS – 1

Match up the player with the number of League goals he scored for Rotherham

611.	Alan Birch	4
612.	Ronnie Burke	8
613.	Alan Kirkman	15
614.	Kevin Kilmore	4
615.	Rodney Johnson	2
616.	Robin Hardy	28
617.	Gerry Gow	8
618.	Dean Emerson	20
619.	Ray Dixon	58
620.	Darren Byfield	56

GERRY FORREST

621. Gerry was born on 21 January in which year – 1955, 1957 or 1959?

622. Gerry played all 38 League games in season 1986/87 for which First Division club?

623. How many League appearances did Gerry make for The Millers – 337, 347 or 357?

624. From 1977 to 1985 Gerry played all 46 League games for Rotherham in which single season – 1978/79, 1980/81 or 1983/84?

625. Gerry scored seven League goals in his Millers career, but how many of those did he score in the 1979/80 season?

626. Where in the north-east was Gerry born?

627. In what position did Gerry play?

628. Which club did Gerry join in August 1990?

629. In 1991 Gerry joined which non-League club?

630. For which club did Gerry make his debut on 7 December 1985, beating Arsenal 3-0 at home?

1950s

631.   How many wins were accrued in Rotherham's 1950/51 Championship win - 30, 31 or 32?

632.   How many goals did Jack Shaw net in the 50 League and Cup matches in season 1950/51 – 26, 36 or 46?

633.   At what stage did Aston Villa put The Millers out of the FA Cup in 1952/53?

634.   Where did Rotherham finish in Division 2 in 1953/54 - 4th, 5th or 9th?

635.   Can you name the four Rotherham players whose League goal tallies were in double figures in 1954/55?

636.   Which side did Rotherham defeat 7-2 away in December 1956?

637.   Rotherham lost 6-0 to which team in an FA Cup 4th round 2nd replay in February 1960?

638.   Which Millers legend was called into the England 'B' squad for the 1952 match against Holland?

639.   Gladdy Guest left Rotherham for which club in 1956?

640.   Who was Rotherham's manager at the close of the decade?

BOBBY WILLIAMSON

641. Bobby was born on 13 August 1961 in which Scottish city?

642. On 19 August 2008 Bobby became the manager of which African national football team?

643. In 1988 Bobby joined Rotherham United from which club?

644. How many League goals did Bobby score for The Millers – 29, 39 or 49?

645. At which Scottish club did Bobby start his professional career in 1980, making 70 League appearances and scoring 28 League goals?

646. Which club did Bobby join in 1986 from Glasgow Rangers for £100,000?

647. In season 1988/89 in Division 4 Bobby netted a hat-trick in May away at which promotion rival club?

648. How many League appearances did Bobby make for Rotherham United – 83, 93 or 103?

649. At which club did Bobby finish his playing career in 1995, only to return a year later as their manager?

650. In 2004/05 Bobby managed Plymouth Argyle, but which manager replaced him when he left in September 2005?

DANNY WILLIAMS

651. In which decade did Danny manage Rotherham United?

652. Danny took over from which Rotherham manager?

653. Which player surpassed Danny's appearances record for Rotherham United in 2007?

654. True or false: Rotherham United was the only club that Danny played for in his career?

655. Which Millers manager gave Danny his Rotherham debut?

656. True or false: Danny won five full international caps for England during his career?

657. In which year did Rotherham reach the FA Cup 5th round, with Danny as a member of the team that beat the holders Newcastle United?

658. Which team did Danny manage after his managerial spell at The Millers?

659. True or false: Danny played for Rotherham throughout the whole of the 1950s?

660. In which year was Danny born in South Yorkshire – 1922, 1923 or 1924?

DAVE WATSON

661. Dave was born on 5 October in Stapleford, Nottinghamshire, in which year – 1946, 1948 or 1950?

662. At which club did Dave start his professional career in 1966?

663. Dave made his England debut against which country in 1973, in an away friendly that would be Sir Alf Ramsey's last game in charge?

664. In 1970 Dave transferred from Rotherham to Sunderland for what fee?

665. In his two years at the club how many League appearances did Dave make for The Millers – 111, 121 or 131?

666. Which honour did Dave win with Manchester City in 1976, beating Newcastle United 2-1?

667. Which manager signed Dave for Rotherham United in 1968?

668. In what position did Dave originally play at Rotherham before moving to centre half?

669. Which honour did Dave win with Sunderland in 1973, beating Leeds United 1-0?

670. In his 65 appearances at international level for England how many goals did Dave score?

2007/2008 - 2

671. From which club did Derek Holmes join Rotherham United?

672. Which match attracted the biggest home League attendance of 6,709?

673. Who ended The Millers' run of seven straight League wins?

674. Which team put Rotherham out of the FA Cup?

675. Keeper Andy Warrington signed for Rotherham from which club?

676. Which side did Rotherham beat in the opening round of the Johnstone's Paint Trophy?

677. In what position did Rotherham finish in the final League table?

678. Who played all 46 League games during the season?

679. To which team did United lose 5-1 away during March 2008?

680. During the end of 2007 how many consecutive League matches did Rotherham win?

MIKE POLLITT

681. Mike was born on 29 February 1972 in which northern county?

682. In what position does Mike play?

683. In June 2001 Mike signed for Rotherham United from which club for £75,000?

684. In Mike's two spells with The Millers (1998-2000 and 2001-05) how many League appearances did he make – 249, 259 or 269?

685. In June 2005 Mike was transferred to Wigan Athletic for what fee?

686. At which club did Mike first play a professional game in 1992?

687. While at Rotherham Mike registered a clean sheets club record of how many – 67, 72 or 77?

688. In the 2006 League Cup final for Wigan Athletic Mike was substituted in the 15th minute by which player?

689. At which club did Mike start his career as a trainee in 1990?

690. At which Lancashire club did Mike spend a month on loan in early 2007?

POT LUCK – 2

691.   Who scored 130 goals for Rotherham between 1946
        and 1956?

692.   Rotherham played four FA Cup games in 1950/51, with
        Jack Shaw scoring how many times?

693.   Which three Rotherham players did referee Tony Leake
        send off in a 1997 match against Swindon?

694.   Who took over as Rotherham manager in September
        1986?

695.   How many League goals did Rotherham score in the
        1946/47 season - 110, 112 or 114?

696.   How many players did The Millers use in League
        matches during 1996/97 - 30, 32 or 34?

697.   How much did Rotherham pay for John Mullen in
        2001?

698.   True or false: The Millers conceded 28 goals in five
        League games in 1929/30 immediately after beating
        Barrow 7-0?

699.   From which club did Rotherham sign Paulo Vernazza in
        July 2004?

700.   Which three keepers did Rotherham use in the 1997
        League match against Shrewsbury?

PAUL STANCLIFFE

701. Paul was born in Sheffield on 5 May in which year –
1954, 1956 or 1958?

702. Against which team did Paul make his Rotherham
United debut in August 1975?

703. In what position did Paul play?

704. How many League goals did Paul score for The Millers
– 5, 7 or 9?

705. At which club did Paul finish his playing career in
1994?

706. Which club did Paul join in August 1983, going on to
make 278 League appearances and scoring 12 League
goals?

707. How many League appearances did Paul make for
Rotherham in his two spells with the club – 280, 285
or 290?

708. Which Millers manager signed Paul on loan in
September 1990?

709. Paul made 17 League appearances for which club in
season 1990/91?

710. As of 2008, at which club is Paul the youth team
coach?

JOHNNY QUINN

711.   Which Rotherham manager signed Johnny for the club?

712.   In what position did Johnny play during his playing days?

713.   In what year was Johnny signed for The Millers and made club captain?

714.   What was Johnny's nickname while at Rotherham?

715.   From which team did Johnny sign to join Rotherham United?

716.   In which year was Johnny born –1938, 1939 or 1940?

717.   In 1968, Rotherham fans gave Johnny his own song, called what?

718.   Which team did Johnny join in 1972 when he left The Millers?

719.   How many League appearances did Johnny make for Rotherham in his career – 104, 114 or 124?

720.   How many League goals did Johnny score in his Rotherham career – 5, 7 or 9?

ALAN LEE

721. Alan was born on 21 August 1978 in which Southern Irish town?

722. Alan moved from Rotherham to Cardiff City in August 2003, for what transfer fee?

723. How many League appearances did Alan make for The Millers in his three years at the club – 111, 121 or 131?

724. At which club did Alan start his career in 1995, although he never made the first team?

725. In 2001 Alan scored a last-minute winning goal, resulting in a 2-1 home win and securing promotion to the Championship, against which side?

726. In January 2006 which club did Alan join for £100,000?

727. How many League goals did Alan score for The Millers – 17, 27 or 37?

728. Which London club did Alan join in August 2008?

729. In what position does Alan play?

730. In April 2003 Alan earned his first full international cap for the Republic of Ireland against which country?

POT LUCK – 3

731. How many League goals did Wally Ardron score in the1946/47 season?

732. How many goals did Jack Shaw score against Darlington in a 1950 FA Cup tie?

733. To which club did Rotherham lose 1-10 in a Division 3 North match in March 1929?

734. Which visiting club in 2003 chose to change in a hotel rather than use the Millmoor dressing rooms?

735. Rotherham lost 0-7 in a 1995 League match against which team?

736. How much did Rotherham get for Alan Lee from Cardiff City in 2003?

737. Which Yorkshire club did Rotherham beat 2-1 in the fourth round of the FA Cup in January 1946?

738. Which Jamaican international played for Rotherham in season 2004/05?

739. Who scored one goal in the game and two in a penalty shoot out in the 2003 Carling Cup match against Arsenal?

740. What was the penalty shootout score in that match?

JIM MCDONAGH

741.   Jim was born on 6 October 1952 in which Yorkshire town?

742.   What is Jim's nickname?

743.   At which club did Jim start his professional career in 1970?

744.   In August 1976 Jim joined Bolton Wanderers, for what transfer fee - £100,000, £150,000 or £200,000?

745.   How many League appearances did Jim make for The Millers – 111, 121 or 131?

746.   In the Second Division Championship winning side of 1977/78 how many League goals did Jim concede in 42 matches – 27, 30 or 33?

747.   In July 1980 which club signed Jim for £250,000?

748.   In 1985 which two clubs signed Jim on loan?

749.   In 1988 Jim was appointed player/manger of which Irish club, saving them from relegation?

750.   For which club, in his two playing spells there, did Jim make 242 League appearances?

LEAGUE GOALSCORERS – 2

Match up the player with the number of League goals he scored for Rotherham

741.	Alan Knill	12
742.	Barry Lyons	2
743.	Brian Tiler	5
744.	Nathan Peel	6
745.	Mike O'Grady	23
746.	Peter Nix	27
747.	Harry Mills	5
748.	John McCole	4
749.	Joe McBride	2
750.	Gary Martindale	3

LOL MORGAN

761. Lol was born on 5 May 1931 in which Yorkshire town?

762. At which club did Lol start his professional career in 1949?

763. What was Lol's nickname?

764. From which club did Lol join Rotherham United in 1951?

765. How many League appearances did Lol make for The Millers – 271, 281 or 291?

766. How many League goals did Lol score for The Millers – 0, 3 or 6?

767. Which club did Lol join in 1964, where he made 30 League appearances?

768. Which club did Lol manage between 1966 and 1969?

769. In what position did Lol play?

770. Lol was in the Rotherham team that lost the League Cup final over two legs against Aston Villa in 1961. What was the aggregate result of these games?

POT LUCK – 4

771.   When Rotherham United were a newly merged club
        what colours were their first kit?

772.   What was the combined fee received from Watford for
        Lee Williamson and Will Hoskins during the 2000s?

773.   What was the name of the club's training ground sold
        in 2006?

774.   Who was sacked as manager after 17 winless matches
        in 2005?

775.   At which West Country club did Jim Furnell finish his
        playing career in 1976?

776.   In what League did Thornhill United originally
        complete?

777.   When Rotherham County were elected to Division 2 in
        1919, of what League were they champions?

778.   In what year did the club adopt the Arsenal-style kit of
        red shirts with white sleeves?

779.   True or false: Rotherham beat Chelsea 6-0 and 4-1 in
        the 1981/82 Division 2 matches?

780.   Where was Eugene Bopp born?

MATCH THE YEAR – 3

Match up the event with the year it took place

781.	Wally Ardron scored 38 League goals in 40 games	1995
782.	Drewe Broughton was born	1953
783.	Frank Casper played the last of his 116 League games for Rotherham United	2007
784.	Mark Robins became manager of The Millers	1987
785.	Andy Todd was born	1998
786.	Nike supplied the kit for Rotherham United	1946
787.	Rotherham legend Gladstone Guest passed away	2005
788.	Paul Blades was born	1967
789.	Alan Crawford was born	1978
790.	Dave Cusack became manager of Rotherham United	1974

LEAGUE GOALSCORERS – 3

Match up the player with the number of League goals he scored for Rotherham

791.	David Artell	1
792.	John Woodall	11
793.	Ian Wilson	4
794.	Ken Houghton	20
795.	Nigel Jemson	6
796.	Glyn Jones	9
797.	Harold Mosby	5
798.	Jimmy Rudd	5
799.	Gordon Swann	56
800.	Roy Tunks	45

ANSWERS

HISTORY OF THE CLUB

1. 1925
2. Rotherham Town and Rotherham County (May 1925)
3. The Millers
4. Millmoor
5. Billy Heald
6. Birmingham City (champions) and Luton Town (runners-up)
7. Barnsley
8. Arthur Wharton
9. Southampton
10. 17

WHO AM I?

11. Roy Tunks
12. Des Hazel
13. Tom McAlister
14. Tony Towner
15. Alan Knill
16. Andy Roscoe
17. Trevor Phillips
18. Drewe Broughton
19. Mike Pickering
20. Wally Ardron

CLUB RECORDS

21. Sheffield United
22. Bradford City
23. Danny Williams
24. Jack Shaw
25. Rotherham United 8-0 Oldham Athletic
26. 114
27. Gladstone Guest
28. 9
29. Scunthorpe United
30. The League Cup

THE LEAGUE CUP

31. Leicester City

32.   George Darwin
33.   Liverpool
34.   Huddersfield Town
35.   Nottingham Forest
36.   York City
37.   Richard Finney
38.   5th
39.   Scunthorpe United
40.   Norwich City

CLUB HONOURS

41.	League Cup runners-up	1961
42.	Auto Windscreens Shield winners	1996
43.	Division 3 champions	1981
44.	Division 3 North champions	1951
45.	Division 2 runners-up	2001
46.	Division 3 runners-up	2000
47.	Division 4 champions	1989
48.	Division 3 North runners-up	1948
49.	Division 4 runners-up	1992
50.	Reached the FA Cup 5th round	1968

PAUL WARNE

51.   Striker
52.   1999
53.   28
54.   Ronnie Moore
55.   Reading
56.   1973
57.   True
58.   Leyton Orient
59.   8 (1999/00)
60.   Oldham Athletic

WHERE DID THEY GO? – 1

61.	Les Bradd	Notts County
62.	Ronnie Moore	Charlton Athletic
63.	Clive Mendonca	Sheffield United

64.	Neil Warnock	Hartlepool United
65.	Alan Crawford	Chesterfield
66.	Deon Burton	Sheffield Wednesday
67.	Alan Lee	Cardiff City
68.	Bob Delgado	Chester City
69.	Ronnie Burke	Exeter City
70.	Wally Ardron	Nottingham Forest

2008/2009

71. Mark Robins
72. Hartlepool United
73. Lincoln City
74. Reuben Reid
75. True: won 3 and drew 1
76. Andy Todd
77. Jamie Clarke and Jamie Green
78. 4-1 to Rotherham
79. Micky Cummins
80. Mark Oxley

MANAGERS – 1

81.	Danny Bergara	1996-97
82.	Billy Heald	1925-29
83.	Ronnie Moore	1997-2005
84.	Alan Knill	2005-07
85.	Ian Porterfield	1979-81
86.	Reg Freeman	1934-52
87.	Tom Johnston	1958-62
88.	Jimmy McAnearney	1968-73
89.	George Kerr	1983-85
90.	Jimmy McGuigan	1973-79

2007/2008

91. Hereford United
92. Mark Robins
93. Andy Warrington
94. False: won 3, drew 1 and lost 1
95. Peter Holmes and Marc Joseph

96. Derek Holmes
97. 9th
98. Ryan Taylor
99. Barnet
100. Jamie Green

NATIONALITIES – 1

101.	Shaun Goater	Bermudian
102.	Toumani Diagouraga	French
103.	Adem Poric	Australian
104.	Jim Dobbin	Scottish
105.	Eugen Bopp	German
106.	Bobby Mimms	English
107.	Bob Delgado	Welsh
108.	Earl Jean	St Lucian
109.	Ray Mielczarek	Welsh
110.	Jim McDonagh	Irish

LEAGUE GOALS

111.	Wally Ardron	98 goals
112.	Jack Grainger	112 goals
113.	Alan Kirkman	58 goals
114.	Ronnie Burke	56 goals
115.	Trevor Phillips	80 goals
116.	Alan Crawford	49 goals
117.	Albert Bennett	64 goals
118.	Shaun Goater	70 goals
119.	Ian Wilson	45 goals
120.	Jack Shaw	123 goals

WHERE DID THEY COME FROM? – 1

121.	Scott Minto	West Ham United
122.	Shaun Goater	Manchester United
123.	Mark Burchill	Dunfermline Athletic
124.	Leo Fortune-West	Brentford
125.	Andy Todd	Accrington Stanley
126.	Paolo Vernazza	Watford
127.	Paul Warne	Wigan Athletic

128.	Mark Robins	Walsall
129.	Paul Blades	Wolverhampton Wanderers
130.	Jim Furnell	Arsenal

LEGENDS

131.	Gerry Forrest
132.	John Breckin
133.	Roy Lambert
134.	Dave Watson
135.	Jimmy Rudd
136.	Alan Lee
137.	Mark Robins
138.	Shaun Goater
139.	Tony Towner
140.	Jack Shaw

LEAGUE POSITIONS - 1

141.	2000/01, 91 points	2nd
142.	1951/52, 42 points	9th
143.	1965/66, 46 points	7th
144.	1982/83, 45 points	20th
145.	1993/94, 58 points	15th
146.	1996/97, 35 points	23rd
147.	1954/55, 54 points	3rd
148.	1962/63, 40 points	14th
149.	1995/96, 56 points	16th
150.	1959/60, 47 points	8th

ATTENDANCES

151.	12,226
152.	31,201
153.	Hull City
154.	Hillsborough
155.	664
156.	False: it was Sunderland
157.	West Ham United
158.	27,451
159.	Leeds United

160.   Bradford City (away, 13,436)

LEAGUE POSITIONS - 2

161.	1968/69, 45 points	11th
162.	1985/86, 57 points	14th
163.	1990/91, 42 points	23rd
164.	1999/2000, 84 points	2nd
165.	1976/77, 59 points	4th
166.	1972/73, 41 points	21st
167.	1998/99, 73 points	5th
168.	1970/71, 50 points	8th
169.	1980/81, 61 points	1st
170.	1983/84, 54 points	18th

2006/2007

171.   13
172.   Crewe Alexandra
173.   Oldham Athletic
174.   v. Nottingham Forest (away)
175.   Will Hoskins
176.   10
177.   Rosehill Press
178.   Peterborough United
179.   Watford
180.   6

SQUAD NUMBERS 2008/2009 – 1

181.	Ryan Taylor	20
182.	Ian Sharps	5
183.	Andy Todd	14
184.	Andy Warrington	1
185.	Jamie Yates	16
186.	Pablo Mills	25
187.	Peter Holmes	8
188.	Mark Lynch	3
189.	Michael Cummins	7
190.	Tom Cahill	21

GOALKEEPERS

191.	Roy Ironside
192.	Kelham O'Hanlon
193.	Halifax Town
194.	Kevin Pilkington
195.	Tom McAlister
196.	Matt Clarke
197.	Mike Pollitt
198.	Stoke City
199.	Germany (Wuppertal)
200.	Billy Mercer

WHERE DID THEY GO? – 2

201.	Will Hoskins	Watford
202.	Bobby Ham	Bradford City
203.	Robbie Stockdale	Hull City
204.	David Artell	Mansfield Town
205.	Tommy Tynan	Plymouth Argyle
206.	Jackie Bestall	Grimsby Town
207.	Don Weston	Leeds United
208.	Terry Farmer	York City
209.	Darren Byfield	Sunderland
210.	Jim Dobbin	Doncaster Rovers

TONY TOWNER

211.	Winger (midfielder)
212.	Brighton & Hove Albion
213.	1980
214.	John Seasman
215.	Ian Porterfield
216.	11
217.	1955
218.	Charlton Athletic
219.	Wolverhampton Wanderers
220.	Tiger

MANAGERS – 2

| 221. | Billy McEwan | 1988-91 |

222.	Mick Harford	2005
223.	Stan Davies	1929-30
224.	Tommy Docherty	1967-68
225.	Emlyn Hughes	1981-83
226.	Andy Smailes	1952-58
227.	Billy Heald	1930-33
228.	Norman Hunter	1985-87
229.	Jack Mansell	1965-67
230.	Danny Williams	1962-65

UNUSUAL SOURCES

231.	Carl Airey	Charleroi
232.	José Miranda	Felgueiras
233.	John Hunter	Coltness United
234.	Jack Edwards	Manvers Main Colliery
235.	Barry Burns	Dunscroft
236.	Dennis Churms	Spurley Hey
237.	James Marsden	Parkgate Welfare
238.	John Quairney	Girvan Juniors
239.	Danny Bolton	Owen and Dyson
240.	Roy Ironside	Atlas and Norfolk

WHERE DID THEY COME FROM? – 2

241.	Derek Holmes	Carlisle United
242.	Neil Cutler	Stockport County
243.	Jimmy Rudd	Leeds United
244.	Michael Jeffrey	Newcastle United
245.	Ian Sharps	Tranmere Rovers
246.	Richie Barker	Macclesfield Town
247.	Michael Proctor	Sunderland
248.	Tommy Spencer	Lincoln City
249.	Alan Knill	Scunthorpe United
250.	Lee Glover	Port Vale

1990s

251.	Crewe Alexandra
252.	Imre Varadi
253.	11th

254. 35,235
255. Nigel Jemson
256. Carl Muggleton
257. Blackpool
258. King's Lynn
259. Mike Pollitt
260. Leo Fortune-West and Paul Warne

SQUAD NUMBERS 2008/2009 - 2

261.	Dale Tonge	2
262.	Mark Hudson	10
263.	Steven Cann	30
264.	Mark Burchill	9
265.	Nick Fenton	6
266.	Marc Joseph	12
267.	Jamie Green	19
268.	Danny Harrison	4
269.	Stephen Brogan	11
270.	Alex Rhodes	15

2005/2006

271. Mick Harford
272. Chesterfield
273. Accrington Stanley
274. Leeds United
275. Deon Burton
276. v. Nottingham Forest
277. Shaun Barker
278. 3-4
279. Richie Barker
280. Gary Montgomery and Neil Cutler

FA CUP WINS

281.	2000/01, round 2	Rotherham United 1-0 Northampton Town
282.	1992/93, round 2	Rotherham United 1-0 Hull City

ﾃ

283.	1978/79, round 1	Rotherham United 3-0 Workington
284.	1967/68, round 4	Aston Villa 0-1 Rotherham United
285.	1985/86, round 2	Rotherham United 4-1 Burnley
286.	1950/51, round 3	Rotherham United 2-1 Doncaster Rovers
287.	1959/60, round 3 2nd replay	Rotherham United 2-0 Arsenal
288.	1970/71, round 2	Grantham 1-4 Rotherham United
289.	2001/02, round 3	Rotherham United 2-1 Southampton
290.	1933/34, round 2	Rotherham United 2-1 Coventry City

TOMMY DOCHERTY

291. 1928
292. Gorbals, Glasgow
293. Shettleston Juniors
294. Arsenal
295. Jack Mansell
296. Queens Park Rangers
297. FC Porto
298. 25
299. South Melbourne and Sydney Olympic
300. Altrincham

PLAYING YEARS AT THE CLUB – 1

301.	Paul Hurst	1993-2008
302.	Jim McDonagh	1970-76
303.	Tony Towner	1980-83
304.	Jack Shaw	1946-53
305.	Trevor Phillips	1968-79
306.	Johnny Quinn	1967-72
307.	Peter Madden	1955-66
308.	Roy Lambert	1954-65

309.	John Galley	1964-68
310.	Alan Lee	2000-03

MILLMOOR

311.	1907
312.	Red House
313.	Greyhound racing
314.	The former Tivoli Picture House stood there
315.	True
316.	Railway End
317.	101 years
318.	1960
319.	Ken Booth
320.	Japanese Knotweed

TOP GOALSCORERS

321.	Gladstone Guest	130
322.	Albert Bennett	64
323.	Wally Ardron	98
324.	Jack Shaw	123
325.	Trevor Phillips	82
326.	John Galley	46
327.	Jack Grainger	112
328.	Shaun Goater	86
329.	Ronnie Moore	52
330.	Ronnie Burke	56

JOHN BRECKIN

331.	Sheffield
332.	1953
333.	Bradford City
334.	Brentford
335.	Darlington
336.	Bury
337.	409
338.	Doncaster Rovers
339.	1975/76
340.	Ronnie Moore

POSITIONS THEY PLAYED – 1

341.	Jack Selkirk	Right back
342.	Jock Quairney	Goalkeeper
343.	Norman Noble	Defender
344.	Shaun Goater	Striker
345.	Jim McDonagh	Goalkeeper
346.	Dave Watson	Central defender
347.	Jack Grainger	Winger
348.	Trevor Phillips	Striker
349.	Jim Breckin	Left back
350.	John Galley	Centre forward

2008/2009

351. Reuben Reid
352. Wolverhampton Wanderers
353. Leeds United
354. Stoke City
355. Drewe Broughton
356. Ilkeston Town
357. Stockport County
358. Athletic Bilbao and Logroñés
359. Aldershot Town
360. Chester City

PLAYING YEARS AT THE CLUB – 2

361.	Jack Grainger	1945-57
362.	Bobby Williamson	1988-90
363.	Shaun Goater	1989-96
364.	Gerry Forrest (1st spell)	1977-85
365.	Lol Morgan	1954-64
366.	Mike Pollitt	1998-2005
367.	Ronnie Moore	1980-83
368.	John Breckin	1971-83
369.	Dave Watson	1968-70
370.	Albert Bennett	1961-65

WHO WERE WE PLAYING?

371. Spennymoor United

372.	Nuneaton Borough
373.	New Brighton
374.	Nelson
375.	Workington
376.	Gateshead
377.	Frickley Colliery
378.	Ashington
379.	Stafford Rangers
380.	Boston United

TOP LEAGUE APPEARANCES

381.	Jack Selkirk	427
382.	Danny Williams	492
383.	Paul Hurst	494
384.	Gerry Forrest	394
385.	John Breckin	467
386.	Jack Grainger	352
387.	Norman Noble	292
388.	Mike Pollitt	301
389.	Peter Madden	311
390.	Darren Garner	308

LEAGUE DEBUTS

391.	John Edwards	1946
392.	Des Hazel	1988
393.	Paul Hurst	1993
394.	Jack Grainger	1947
395.	Roy Lambert	1957
396.	Gerry Forrest	1977
397.	Lol Morgan	1955
398.	Peter Madden	1956
399.	Ray Mountford	1979
400.	John Breckin	1971

POSITIONS THEY PLAYED – 2

401.	Jack Edwards	Wing half
402.	Paul Stancliffe	Central defender
403.	Gerry Forrest	Right back

404.	Wally Ardron	Striker
405.	Paul Hurst	Defender
406.	Peter Madden	Centre half
407.	Mike Pollitt	Goalkeeper
408.	Mark Robins	Striker
409.	Jack Shaw	Centre forward
410.	Lol Morgan	Left back

1980s

411.	Ian Porterfield
412.	Southend United
413.	Joe McBride
414.	24
415.	Boston United
416.	George Kerr
417.	Kevin Kilmore
418.	Burnley
419.	Tommy Tynan
420.	Mick Gooding

MATCH THE YEAR – 1

421.	Rotherham began playing their home games at Sheffield's Don Valley Stadium	2008
422.	Rotherham beat Spennymoor United 6-0 in the FA Cup 2nd round	1977
423.	T-Mobile became Rotherham's sponsors for the first time	1999
424.	Shaun Goater joined Rotherham United	1989
425.	Clive Mendonca was born	1968
426.	Rotherham ended the season with 91 points in Division 2	2001
427.	Ronnie Moore became manager of The Millers	1997
428.	The Millers were the runners-up in Division 3 North	1949
429.	Rotherham escaped relegation on goal difference	2002
430.	Scott Minto was born	1971

SIGNED FROM WHERE?

431.	Mick Pickering	Sheffield Wednesday
432.	Earl Jean	Ipswich Town
433.	Jimmy Mullen	Charlton Athletic
434.	Andy Roscoe	Bolton Wanderers
435.	Clive Mendonca	Sheffield United
436.	Michael Proctor	Sunderland
437.	Toumani Diagouraga	Watford
438.	Julian Baudet	Oldham Athletic
439.	Trevor Berry	Aston Villa
440.	Andy Todd	Accrington Stanley

MATCH THE YEAR – 2

441.	Reuben Reid joined The Millers	2008
442.	Lee Glovers signs for Rotherham United.	1996
443.	Danny Williams left Rotherham United	1966
444.	Tony Towner was born	1955
445.	Emlyn Hughes joined Rotherham from Wolverhampton Wanderers	1981
446.	Jim Furnell left The Millers to join Plymouth Argyle	1970
447.	Neil Warnock joined Rotherham from Chesterfield	1969
448.	Chris Sedgwick made his 244th League appearance for the club	2004
449.	Andy Warrington was born	1976
450.	Nigel Jemson came to Rotherham on loan and made 16 League appearances, scoring 5 goals	1996

1970s

451. Trevor Phillips
452. Steve Downes
453. Great Harwood
454. Ray Mielczarek
455. FC Bruges, Sparta Rotterdam and NAC Breda
456. Carl Gilbert (he went in goal to replace Jim McDonagh)
457. Crewe Alexandra
458. Alan Crawford
459. Mossley and Spennymoor United

460.   Jimmy McGuigan

CAPS FOR MY COUNTRY

461.	Shaun Goater	36 caps for Bermuda
462.	Dave Watson	65 caps for England
463.	Alan Knill	1 cap for Wales
464.	Bruce Dyer	1 cap for Montserrat
465.	Alan Lee	10 caps for Republic of Ireland
466.	Emlyn Hughes	62 caps for England
467.	Mark Burchill	6 caps for Scotland
468.	Jackie Bestall	1 cap for England
469.	Colin Murdock	34 caps for Northern Ireland
470.	Jim McDonagh	24 caps for Republic of Ireland

YEAR OF BIRTH

471.	Jack Grainger	1924
472.	Graham Coughlan	1974
473.	Gerry Gow	1952
474.	Roy Ironside	1935
475.	Barry Cowdrill	1957
476.	Dave Gwyther	1948
477.	Phil Gridelet	1967
478.	Scott Minto	1971
479.	Paul Stancliffe	1958
480.	Guy Branston	1979

NATIONALITIES – 2

481.	Omar Garcia	Spanish
482.	Steven Cann	Welsh
483.	Mark Burchill	Scottish
484.	Michael Cummins	Irish
485.	Lee Williamson	Jamaican
486.	Bruce Dyer	Montserratian
487.	Alan Knill	Welsh
488.	Colin Murdock	Northern Irish
489.	Dick Habbin	English
490.	Leandre Griffit	French

PHIL HENSON

491.	Manchester City
492.	Sheffield Wednesday
493.	Sparta Rotterdam
494.	1953
495.	Stockport County
496.	Division 3
497.	Ian Porterfield
498.	Billy McEwan
499.	2nd
500.	Archie Gemmill and John McGovern

TRANSFERS

501.	Mike Pollitt to Rotherham United 2001	£75,000
502.	Albert Bennett to Newcastle United 1965	£27,000
503.	Deon Burton to Rotherham United 2005	Free
504.	Clive Mendonca to Rotherham United 1988	£35,000
505.	Alan Lee to Rotherham United 2000	£150,000
506.	Dave Watson to Sunderland 1970	£100,000
507.	Leo Fortune-West to Rotherham United 1999	£35,000
508.	Jim McDonagh to Bolton Wanderers 1976	£150,000
509.	Shaun Goater to Bristol City 1996	£175,000
510.	Darren Garner to Rotherham United 1995	£30,000

HAT-TRICKS

511.	Darren Byfield
512.	Herbert Yates
513.	3
514.	Bobby Williamson
515.	Carl Airey
516.	Leo Fortune-West and Danny Hudson
517.	Earl Jean
518.	2
519.	9
520.	Derek Holmes

SHAUN GOATER

521.	1970

522. Manchester United

523. MBE

524. 282

525. Southend United

526. 70

527. Reading

528. Osasuna

529. Notts County

530. True

DON VALLEY

531. 1991

532. September 1990

533. RM Douglas Construction

534. The Games

535. £29 million

536. Sheffield Eagles, City of Sheffield Athletics Club and Parramore Sports

537. 45 metres

538. Jan Zelezny

539. Derby County

540. Lincoln City

DARREN GARNER

541. Plymouth

542. Plymouth Argyle

543. Midfielder

544. Dorchester Town

545. 249 (16)

546. Torquay United

547. 23

548. He had suffered a broken leg at Reading in March 2001

549. Launceston, Truro City and Bodmin Town

550. Manager of non-League Launceston

BIG WINS

551. Spennymoor United

552. Wolverhampton Wanderers

553. **Millwall**
554. *1947*
555. **Peterborough United**
556. **Wigan Athletic**
557. **Barrow**
558. **Scunthorpe United**
559. **Carlisle United**
560. **True**

MARK ROBINS
561. *1969*
562. **Manchester United**
563. *£800,000*
564. **Arsenal**
565. **Alan Knill**
566. *84 (23)*
567. **The FA Cup**
568. *6*
569. *44*
570. **Burton Albion**

1960s
571. **Shrewsbury Town**
572. **Alan Kirkman**
573. **Albert Bennett**
574. **Brian Tiler**
575. **Bury**
576. *1967/68*
577. **Boston Beacons**
578. **Sheffield Wednesday**
579. *£45,000*
580. **Finland**

RONNIE MOORE
581. **Liverpool**
582. *22*
583. **Tranmere Rovers**
584. **Cardiff City**

585. 52
586. 125
587. Central defender
588. Rochdale
589. Tranmere Rovers
590. Danny Bergara

POT LUCK -1
591. 1925/26
592. Chesterfield
593. Thornhill United
594. Shaun Goater
595. Kevin Eley (16 years and 72 days)
596. New Zealander
597. Dave Cusack
598. Midland League
599. Anton Johnson
600. Tony Towner

PAUL HURST
601. Sheffield
602. Hursty
603. 385 (51)
604. Burton Albion
605. Left back
606. 13
607. Auto Windscreens Shield
608. 494
609. Rotherham United
610. Mansfield Town

LEAGUE GOALSCORERS - 1
611. Alan Birch   28
612. Ronnie Burke   56
613. Alan Kirkman   58
614. Kevin Kilmore   20
615. Rodney Johnson   8
616. Robin Hardy   2

617.	Gerry Gow	4
618.	Dean Emerson	8
619.	Ray Dixon	4
620.	Darren Byfield	15

GERRY FORREST

621.	1957
622.	Southampton
623.	357
624.	1978/79
625.	4
626.	Stockton-on-Tees
627.	Right back
628.	Rotherham United
629.	Gateshead
630.	Southampton

1950s

631.	31
632.	46
633.	5th round
634.	5th
635.	Jack Grainger (19), Ronnie Burke (17), Ian Wilson (17) and Gladdy Guest (14)
636.	Sheffield United
637.	Brighton
638.	Jack Grainger
639.	Gainsborough Trinity
640.	Tom Johnston

BOBBY WILLIAMSON

641.	Glasgow
642.	Uganda
643.	West Bromwich Albion
644.	49
645.	Clydebank
646.	West Bromwich Albion
647.	Crewe Alexandra

648.   93

649.   Kilmarnock

650.   Tony Pulis

DANNY WILLIAMS

651.   1960s (1962-65)

652.   Tom Johnston

653.   Paul Hurst

654.   True

655.   Reg Freeman

656.   False: he did not win any caps

657.   1953

658.   Swindon Town

659.   True: from 1943 to 1960

660.   1924

DAVE WATSON

661.   1946

662.   Notts County

663.   Portugal

664.   £100,000

665.   121

666.   The League Cup

667.   Tommy Docherty

668.   Midfielder

669.   The FA Cup

670.   8

2007/2008 – 2

671.   Carlisle United

672.   v. Wycombe Wanderers

673.   Rochdale

674.   Forest Green Rovers

675.   Bury

676.   Mansfield Town

677.   9th

678.   Andy Warrington

679.   Morecambe

680.	8

MIKE POLLITT

681.	Lancashire (Farnworth)
682.	Goalkeeper
683.	Chesterfield
684.	269
685.	£200,000
686.	Lincoln City
687.	77
688.	John Filan
689.	Manchester United
690.	Burnley

POT LUCK – 2

691.	Gladstone Guest
692.	9
693.	Vance Warner, Lee Glover and Neil Richardson
694.	Danny Bergara
695.	114
696.	34
697.	£150,000
698.	True
699.	Watford
700.	Bobby Mimms (injured), Neil Richardson (sent off) and Steve Thompson

PAUL STANCLIFFE

701.	1958
702.	Brighton & Hove Albion
703.	Central defender
704.	7
705.	York City
706.	Sheffield United
707.	290
708.	Billy McEwan
709.	Wolverhampton Wanderers
710.	Doncaster Rovers

JOHNNY QUINN

711. Tommy Docherty
712. Midfielder
713. 1967
714. The Mighty Quinn
715. Sheffield Wednesday
716. 1938
717. 'Quinn the Eskimo (The Mighty Quinn)'
718. Halifax Town
719. 114
720. 7

ALAN LEE

721. Galway
722. £850,000
723. 111
724. Aston Villa
725. Brentford
726. Ipswich Town
727. 37
728. Crystal Palace
729. Striker
730. Norway

POT LUCK – 3

731. 38
732. 5
733. South Shields
734. West Ham United
735. Wrexham
736. £900,000
737. Barnsley
738. Jamal Campbell-Ryce
739. Gary Montgomery
740. 9-8 to Arsenal

JIM McDONAGH

741. Rotherham

742. Seamus
743. Rotherham United
744. £150,000
745. 121
746. 33
747. Everton
748. Gillingham and Sunderland
749. Galway United
750. Bolton Wanderers

LEAGUE GOALSCORERS - 2

751.	Alan Knill	5
752.	Barry Lyons	23
753.	Brian Tiler	27
754.	Nathan Peel	4
755.	Mike O'Grady	2
756.	Peter Nix	2
757.	Harry Mills	3
758.	John McCole	5
759.	Joe McBride	12
760.	Gary Martindale	6

LOL MORGAN

761. Rotherham
762. Huddersfield Town
763. Lol (real first name is Laurence)
764. Huddersfield Town
765. 291
766. 0
767. Darlington
768. Norwich City
769. Left back
770. Aston Villa 3-2 Rotherham United

POT LUCK - 4

771. Amber and black
772. £1.2 million
773. Hooton Roberts

774. Mick Harford
775. Plymouth Argyle
776. Sheffield and Hallamshire
777. Midland League
778. 1946
779. True
780. Kiev, Ukraine

MATCH THE YEAR – 3

781.	Wally Ardron scored 38 League goals in 40 games	1946
782.	Drewe Broughton was born	1978
783.	Frank Casper played the last of his 116 League games for Rotherham United	1967
784.	Mark Robins became manager of The Millers	2007
785.	Andy Todd was born	1974
786.	Nike supplied the kit for Rotherham United	2005
787.	Rotherham legend Gladstone Guest passed away	1998
788.	Paul Blades was born	1995
789.	Alan Crawford was born	1953
790.	Dave Cusack became manager of Rotherham United	1987

LEAGUE GOALSCORERS - 3

791.	David Artell	4
792.	John Woodall	5
793.	Ian Wilson	45
794.	Ken Houghton	56
795.	Nigel Jemson	5
796.	Glyn Jones	6
797.	Harold Mosby	9
798.	Jimmy Rudd	11
799.	Gordon Swann	1
800.	Roy Tunks	20

NOTES

NOTES

NOTES

NOTES

NOTES

NOTES

NOTES

OTHER BOOKS BY CHRIS COWLIN:

* Celebrities' Favourite Football Teams

* The British TV Sitcom Quiz Book

* The Cricket Quiz Book

* The Gooners Quiz Book

* The Official Aston Villa Quiz Book

* The Official Birmingham City Quiz Book

* The Official Brentford Quiz Book

* The Official Bristol Rovers Quiz Book

* The Official Burnley Quiz Book

* The Official Bury Quiz Book

* The Official Carlisle United Quiz Book

* The Official Carry On Quiz Book

* The Official Chesterfield Football Club Quiz Book

* The Official Colchester United Quiz Book

* The Official Coventry City Quiz Book

* The Official Doncaster Rovers Quiz Book

* The Official Greenock Morton Quiz Book

The Official Heart of Midlothian Quiz Book

* The Official Hereford United Quiz Book

* The Official Hull City Quiz Book

OTHER BOOKS BY CHRIS COWLIN:

* The Official Leicester City Quiz Book

* The Official Macclesfield Town Quiz Book

* The Official Norwich City Football Club Quiz

* The Official Notts County Quiz Book

* The Official Peterborough United Quiz Book

* The Official Port Vale Quiz Book

* The Official Rochdale AFC Quiz Book

* The Official Shrewsbury Town Quiz Book

* The Official Stockport County Quiz Book

* The Official Sunderland Quiz Book

* The Official Watford Football Club Quiz Book

* The Official West Bromwich Albion Quiz Book

* The Official Wolves Quiz Book

* The Official Yeovil Town Quiz Book

* The Reality Television Quiz Book

* The Southend United Quiz Book

* The Ultimate Derby County Quiz Book

* The Ultimate Horror Film Quiz Book

* The West Ham United Quiz Book

www.apexpublishing.co.uk